To Vic
Merry Xmas!
Love,
"Roomie"

My Book

_____

_____

D1290210

Kindness is
a lot of things

Story by
Edith Eckblad

Illustrations by
Bonnie & Bill Rutherford

THE C. R. GIBSON COMPANY
NORWALK, CONNECTICUT

To
Barbie,
Janet,
Rick
and Baby Thomas,

for Kindnesses remembered!

Kindness is a lot of things:
 It is a way of thinking,
 and a way of doing.
 It is a way of being . . .
 the way God wants
 you to be.

Kindness can be shown in many ways.
It may be letting your little
brother hold the new baby first!

Sometimes kindness is just
being quiet!

Kindness is telling a friend
that you like him.

Kindness is remembering when
it is time for kitty's dinner.

Kindness is leaving the eggs
in the nest and putting the frog
back in the water!

Kindness is letting the new boy
in your neighborhood walk your dog

or waiting for a little
friend to catch up.

Kindness is helping someone
who can't do something
as well as you.

It is sharing your candy
and letting someone else
have the biggest piece.

Kindness is keeping things pretty
for other people

or noticing a friend's new dress.

Kindness is letting little brother
help, even when the job would be
easier to do by yourself.

It is making someone small
feel BIG!

Kindness is leaving an apple on
a low branch where a small friend
can reach it.

Kindness is reading
"just one more" story.

Kindness is not asking "what is it?"
when someone shows you
his drawing!

Kindness is giving a little
friend a ride in your wagon, even
though she is too small to
return the favor.

It is helping to pick up
around the house.

It is kissing the hurt away.

Kindness is a lot of things:
 It is sharing.
 It is being thoughtful.
 It is being friendly.
 Kindness is a way of
 showing love!

Kindness is a way of being y<u>ou</u> . . .
the <u>you</u> that God wants you to be!